THIS BOOK BELONGS TO:

Baby Shark: Annual 2020

A CENTUM BOOK 978-1-913072-57-5

Published in Great Britain by Centum Books Ltd

This edition published 2019

1 3 5 7 9 10 8 6 4 2

Centum Books Ltd, 20 Devon Square, Newton Abbot, Devon, TQ12 2HR, UK

books@centumbooksltd.co.uk

CENTUM BOOKS Limited Reg. No. 07641486

A CIP catalogue record for this book is available from the British Library.

Printed in Italy.

Contents

Check your answers on pages 76 and 77.

Baby Shark and his family!

Baby Shark

Baby Shark lives under the ocean and is curious about everything around him. He likes to sing. When he's scared, he sings to help him feel brave.

Mummy Shark

There are no limits to the things that Mummy Shark can do! She always listens to Baby Shark and they share a very special bond.

Daddy Shark

Daddy Shark is a strong and mighty hunter. He is much more than just Baby Shark's father though, the two of them play together like best friends!

Grandma Shark

Grandma Shark likes to read. She is a kind and thoughtful grandma who always has time to spend with Baby Shark.

Grandpa Shark

Grandpa Shark is wise and smart. He is famous for his hot clam buns and he loves to share his love of cooking with Baby Shark.

Spot and see!

Can you find
all the things at the
bottom of the picture?
When you spot them,
tick the box!

Baby Shark is dotty!

Finish off Baby Shark and his family by joining the dots and then colouring them in.

Christmas Wonderland

It's Christmas Eve, and the night is pitch-black. Mummy Shark sings a lullaby to Baby Shark.

'Close your eyes. When you wake up, it will be Christmas! Good night, Baby Shark!'

But Baby Shark isn't tired.

'I can't sleep, Mummy,' Baby Shark says.

Daddy Shark rocks the cradle back
and forth.

'Santa Claus won't come until you're sound asleep. Sleep tight, Baby Shark!'
But Baby Shark still isn't tired.
'But I still can't sleep, Daddy,'
Baby Shark says.

Baby Shark's eyes begin to feel heavy. He gently closes his eyes and . . .

18

. . . suddenly, he is in a Christmas Winter Wonderland!

'What a beautiful place!' says Baby Shark.

'Hurry up!'

Baby Shark looks up into the sky.
Rudolph and his friends are pulling
Santa's sleigh across the sky.
Baby Shark is excited and begins to
follow Santa.

'Santa, wait for me!'

CONTINUED ON PAGE 28.

Where's Santa?

Help Baby Shark to find Santa. Use the presents to help you.

START

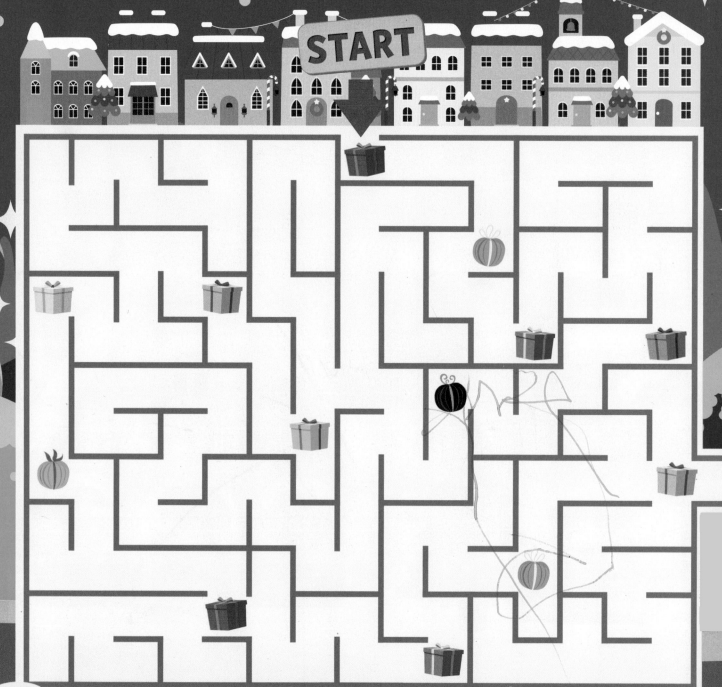

FINISH

Who will you be?

Which member of the Shark family do you want to be?

1 Do you like to sing?

A. Yes, all the time!

B. With my family

C. When I'm scared

D. I prefer to play the flute

E. My voice is very loud!

2 Do like to cook?

A. Not so much

B. Yes!

C. I don't really know how

D. Sometimes

E. Oh, yes! Especially my hot clam buns

3 Do you like to paint?

A. Not really

B. I love it!

C. I like it but sometimes I get a bit messy

D. I'm not as good as my daughter!

E. No

4

Do you like to hunt?

A. I'm the best!

B. Not really

C. If I can go with my dad

D. Not so much

E. I used to!

5

Do you like to read?

A. Sometimes

B. Yes

C. I really like it if someone reads to me

D. Yes, and I like reading to my grandson

E. Of course

Mainly A's:

You're Daddy Shark!
You love to hunt, sing and spend time with your family.

Mainly B's:

You're Mummy Shark!
You love to paint, cook and have fun with your family.

Mainly C's:

You're Baby Shark!
You love to sing, play and read with your grandma.

Mainly D's:

You're Grandma Shark!
You love to have picnics and play with your grandson.

Mainly E's:

You're Grandpa Shark!
You love to cook hot clam buns, sing and look after your family.

25

Who shouldn't be here?

Which sea creature is the odd one out? Circle them with a pen or a pencil.

1

2

3

26

What's different?

Can you spot the five differences between the pictures?

Christmas Wonderland

Continued from page 21.

Santa is counting
the Elves.

'One, two, three, four, five, six!
Great! Get in place
please, everyone!'

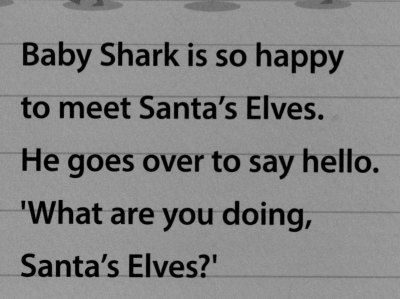

Baby Shark is so happy
to meet Santa's Elves.
He goes over to say hello.
'What are you doing,
Santa's Elves?'

'Hello, Baby Shark!
We are very busy
at the moment as
it's Christmas Eve.'

'We have to wrap all the presents and deliver
them tonight!'

Grandpa Shark tip-toes
in to check on Baby Shark.

'Hush-a-bye,
Baby Shark'

Baby Shark stirs and wakes up.

'Grandpa Shark?'

Grandpa Shark smiles, 'I'll sing you a song
to put you back to sleep, Baby Shark.'

Grandma Shark also comes in to help
Baby Shark fall asleep again.
'I will read to you so you'll have a nice
dream, Baby Shark!' she says.

'Long ago,
in an ocean far away...'

Baby Shark was falling asleep in no time.

Baby Shark is back in the Christmas Winter
Wonderland! He spots Santa again.
'I want to help too, Santa Claus!' says
Baby Shark.

'Ho, ho, ho! Will you help me deliver
Christmas presents to our ocean friends?'
asks Santa.

Baby Shark cries, 'One, two, ho-ho!'
Santa's Elves reply, 'Three, four, here
we go!'

Everyone is working very hard, as together they load the gifts onto Santa's sleigh.

CONTINUED ON PAGE 44.

Spot the Shark family!

Mummy Shark loves putting pictures of the family in her book!

How many times can you see Baby Shark?

How many times can you see Mummy Shark?

How many times can you see Daddy Shark?

How many times can you see Grandma Shark?

How many times can you see Grandpa Shark?

Play it again!

The Shark Family Orchestra have lost their instruments — can you help them? Look closely in the picture and see if you can spot the instruments.

Where is Baby Shark's violin?

Where is Daddy Shark's trumpet?

La, la, la, la, la!

Baby Shark and friends!

Can you find the correct jigsaw pieces to make up the scene?

40

What a muddle!

Everyone has lost something, can you help them find it?

Mummy Shark has lost her glasses.

Daddy Shark has lost his party hat.

Baby Shark has lost his balloon.

Grandpa Shark has lost his banjo.

Grandma Shark has lost her present.

41

Hide and seek

Baby Shark is playing hide and seek with his friends. Draw a line to each sea creature when you find them.

Where is the seahorse?

Where is the crab?

Where is the stingray?

43

christmas
Wonderland

Continued from page 35.

Now it's time to deliver the gifts.
Jingle, jingle!

Santa Claus and Baby Shark both ride
their sleighs into the dark night.

'Baby Shark, doo-doo-doo-doo!'

'It's Christmas, doo-doo-doo-doo!'

'We need to deliver these gifts before morning comes!' says Santa. Baby Shark begins to sing a happy Christmas song.

'Thank you for your help,
Baby Shark! It was a holly, jolly
Christmas Eve!' laughs Santa.

Daddy Shark gently wakes Baby Shark.
'It's Christmas morning, Baby Shark.'

'Baby Shark,
come here!'

'Merry Christmas, Baby Shark!'

Santa must have visited
Baby Shark last night too!

'Merry Christmas, everyone!'
says Baby Shark.

THE END!

Which present?

Guess who each present is for? Draw a line to each one.

Grandpa Shark likes the colour green.

Grandma Shark likes to wear a hat with a bell!

Daddy Shark likes to keep warm.

Mummy Shark likes to jingle.

Baby Shark loves Santa.

Your present!

What would you like for a present? Draw it in the box.

For you

To give

Now you can draw what you'd like to give someone else.

Sing along!

Baby Shark loves to sing. Can you write the words to his song and then sing along too?

Baby Shark,
doo-doo-doo
-doo-doo-doo!

Baby Shark,
doo-doo-doo
-doo-doo-doo!

Baby Shark,
doo-doo-doo
-doo-doo-doo!

Baby Shark!

54

Everyone's making music!

Baby Shark loves to play music with his family. Draw lines to everyone's instrument.

Trumpet

Oboe

Marimba

Flute

Cello

55

Party time!

Baby Shark loves to dress up! Look at all the costumes he has. Choose your favourite and draw it on to him.

56

Shadow sharks

Can you match each shark to their shadow? Who's missing their shadow?

.... Shark's shadow is missing.

Shark names

Fit all the Shark family names into the grid. Some letters have been left to help you!

D (top of vertical word)

G

Y

M

Baby Shark
Mummy Shark
Daddy Shark
Grandma Shark
Grandpa Shark

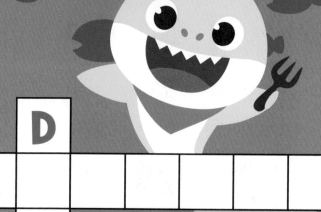

Shark search

How many times can you see the word SHARK in this grid?

S	H	A	R	K	A
H	H	R	A	H	S
A	K	A	S	R	H
R	S	K	R	H	A
K	A	R	A	K	R
S	H	A	R	K	K

SHARK
is in the grid

....

.... times.

59

Odd one out

Look closely at each line-up. One shark
in each line is different to the rest.
Circle them with a pencil.

1

a b c d e

2
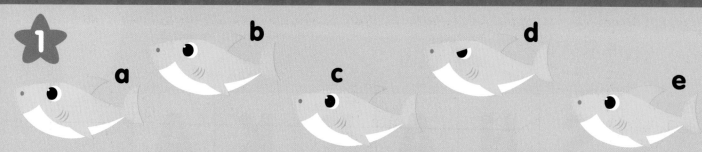

a b c d e

3

a b c d e

4

a b c d e

5

a b c d e

Find the colour!

Colour the picture in using the numbers to help you choose the right colours.

COLOURS

1 White	**3** Pink	**5** Blue	**8** Red
2 Yellow	**4** Purple	**6** Green	**9** Brown
		7 Orange	**10** Black

Learn to draw!

Copy the lines in the grid to draw your own Baby Shark!

Now draw Daddy Shark!

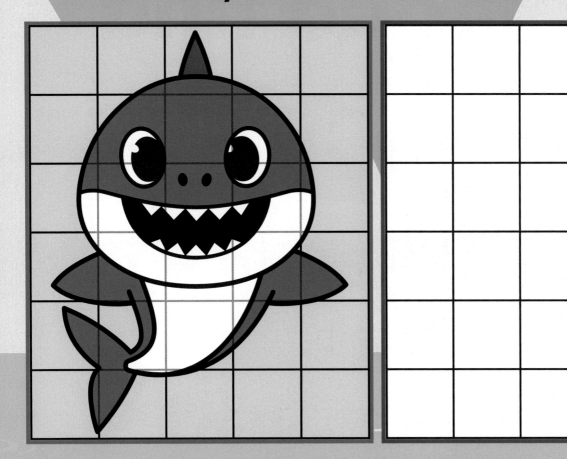

And don't forget Mummy Shark!

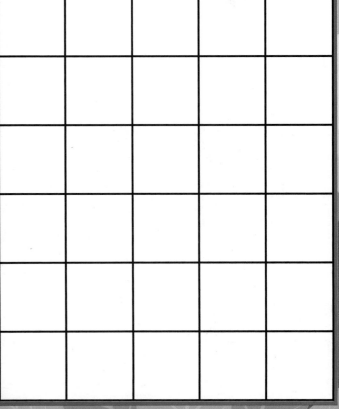

Count and find

64

Can you see:

1		✔
2		
3		
4		
5		
6		
7		
8		
9		
10		

Your own seabed

You can draw your own underwater paradise! The sea creatures and plants around the side are there for you to copy.

Buried treasure

Can you find your way to the casket of buried treasure? Follow the yellow direction arrows and you might find gold!

DIRECTIONS:

6 7 8 9 10

The casket is in square:

....

69

Make your own sea scene

Grandma Shark is here to help you make your very own sea scene!

YOU WILL NEED:

- A big piece of card
- Yellow card or material (optional)
- Pens and colouring pencils
- Glue
- Stones, shells, pipe cleaners
- Smaller pieces of card
- Scissors

Don't forget to ask a grown-up to help you with any cutting out if you use scissors.

INSTRUCTIONS:

🐚 Use the big piece of card for your background.

🐚 Colour the bottom half of the card yellow, for sand, or cut out and stick some yellow paper or material down.

🐚 Now colour the top half blue.

🐚 Use the smaller pieces of card to draw some fish and sea creatures, colour them in and then cut them out and stick them on to the scene.

🐚 Use all sorts of things to decorate your scene: shells, flat stones, sparkly green pipe cleaners (for seaweed).

Sorting colours

Baby Shark loves looking at different colours and sorting them out.

Write down in the boxes below how many of each colour you can see.

Colour	
Red	
Green	
Blue	
Yellow	
Pink	
Orange	

72

Draw the next one

What comes next in the sequence? Can you draw it in?

DRAW

1

2

3

Fish Bus!

Draw Fish Bus's route following the instructions.

BUS

START

INSTRUCTIONS:

The first stop for Fish Bus is by the old shipwreck.

The second stop is just underneath the palm tree.

The third stop is by the pink rock.

The fourth stop is by the red starfish.

BUS

Answers

Pages 22-23

Pages 38-39

Page 26

Page 40

b = 1   d = 2   e = 3   h = 4   c = 5

Page 41

Page 27

Pages 36-37

Baby Shark is shown 6 times.
Mummy Shark is shown 3 times.
Daddy Shark is shown 4 times.
Grandma Shark is shown 4 times.
Grandpa Shark is shown 5 times.

Page 42-43

Page 52

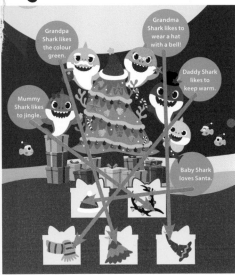

Grandpa Shark likes the colour green.

Grandma Shark likes to wear a hat with a bell!

Daddy Shark likes to keep warm.

Mummy Shark likes to jingle.

Baby Shark loves Santa.

Page 55

Trumpet
Marimba
Oboe
Flute
Cello

Page 57

a = 2   b = 3   c = 5   d = 4
Grandpa Shark's shadow is missing.

Page 58

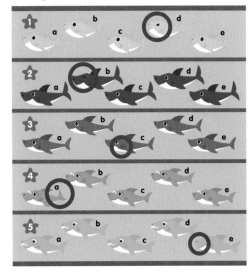

Page 59

Shark is in the grid 5 times.

S	H	A	R	K	A
H	H	R	A	H	S
A	K	A	S	R	H
R	S	K	R	H	A
K	A	R	A	K	R
S	H	A	R	K	K

Page 60

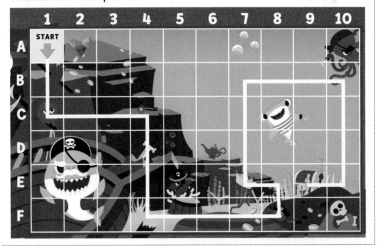

Pages 68–69

The casket is in square E9.

Page 72

Red	7	Yellow	4
Green	9	Pink	9
Blue	7	Orange	7

Page 73

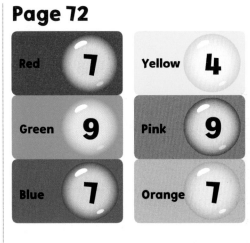

DRAW

Pages 74–75

START

INSTRUCTIONS:

The first stop for Fish Bus is by the old shipwreck.

The second stop is just underneath the palm tree.

The third stop is by the pink rock.

The fourth stop is by the red starfish.

77